How to use this book

Follow the advice, in italics, given for you on each page.
Support the children as they read the text that is shaded in cream.
Praise *the children at every step!*

Detailed guidance is provided in the Read Write Inc. Phonics Handbook.

8 reading activities

Children:
- *Practise reading the speed sounds.*
- *Read the green, red and challenge words for the story.*
- *Listen as you read the introduction.*
- *Discuss the vocabulary check with you.*
- *Read the story.*
- *Re-read the story and discuss the 'questions to talk about'.*
- *Re-read the story with fluency and expression.*
- *Practise reading the speed words.*

Speed sounds

Consonants *Say the pure sounds (do not add 'uh').*

f ff	l (ll)	m	n	r	s ss	v ve	z (zz) s	sh	(th)	ng nk

b bb	c k ck	d	g gg	h	j	p	qu	t	w (wh)	x	y	ch tch

Vowels *Say the vowel sound and then the word, e.g. 'a', 'at'.*

at	hen	in	on	up	day	see	high	blow	zoo

*Each box contains one sound but sometimes more than one grapheme. Focus graphemes are **circled**.*

Green words

Read in Fred Talk (pure sounds).

fi<u>sh</u>   <u>th</u>at   net   pond   but   <u>wh</u>i<u>zz</u>   help   ba<u>ck</u>
from   cub   crept   trap   rip   went

Read the root word first and then with the ending.

Wi<u>ll</u>   →   Wi<u>ll</u>'s

Red words

s<u>ai</u>d   <u>th</u>e   I'<u>ll</u>   to   no   b<u>ear</u>*

* Red word for this book only

Vocabulary check

Discuss the meaning (as used in the story) after the children have read the word.

definition:

bear cub   *a baby bear*

crept   *moved slowly and quietly*

Punctuation to note in this story:

Will	*Capital letters for names*
A Help Put	*Capital letters that start sentences*
.	*Full stop at the end of each sentence*
!	*Exclamation mark used to show anger and surprise*
…	*Wait and see*

Will's net

Introduction

Baby bears are called bear cubs. They love to eat fish.
Will is angry when a bear cub takes a fish from his pond.
So Will decides to catch the bear in his net, but the bear
doesn't want to be caught. Let's see what happens.

Story written by Cynthia Rider
Illustrated by Tim Archbold

A bear cub got a fish from Will's pond.

"Put it back!" said Will.

Grrr! went the cub …

and Will ran.

"I'll get that cub!
I'll trap it
in a net,"
said Will.

Will crept back to the pond. *Whizz!*

Will got the cub in his net.
But the cub went *rip, rip, rip!*

"Help!" said Will.
"No net!"

Grrrr! went the cub and Will ran …

and ran …

and ran.

Questions to talk about

FIND IT QUESTIONS

✓ Turn to the page

✓ Read the question to the children

✓ Find the answer

Page 8: How did Will feel about the cub catching a fish in his pond?
(Look at the picture to help: pleased/cross/furious.)

Page 9: What did the cub do?

Page 10: What did Will decide to do?
How did Will get back to the pond?

Page 11: How did Will feel when the cub ripped through the net?

Page 12-13: What did he do?